TOPLINERS

Sam and Me

Joan Tate

PAN / MACMILLAN

© Joan Tate 1968

330 02014 5

First edition 1968
Reprinted 1968

PAN BOOKS LIMITED
33 Tothill Street London S W 1

MACMILLAN & CO LTD
Little Essex Street London W C 2
and also at Bombay Calcutta and Madras
Macmillan South Africa (Publishers) Pty Ltd Johannesburg
The Macmillan Company of Australia Pty Ltd Melbourne
The Macmillan Company of Canada Ltd Toronto

Printed in Great Britain by
RICHARD CLAY (THE CHAUCER PRESS) LTD
Bungay Suffolk

1

I can't go to sleep. The baby's breathing is like thunder in my ears; long-distance thunder — the kind that doesn't frighten, but which stays there uneasily on the fringe. So I thought I would try to write it all down. Write it out of my system, now that I am here. Now that it has actually happened. Now that the baby is here in my room, with me, lying there in the carry-cot, breathing so that I can hear nothing else.

I have been sitting next to him, just looking at him; just looking at his round head, his thin silk hair, his ears which are indeed like shells, just as it says in all the stories. Pink, curved shells with yellow tips and tiny hairs all round the edges. I can see only one of his hands; the other is hidden underneath him. But the one that shows is clenched tightly, the fingers overlapping the thumb, gripping fiercely. I feel I could sit and look at him for ever. The room is warm and the curtains are drawn and there is no one here but me and the baby. No one.

I think the woman downstairs thinks I am not married and have come here to escape from the neighbours' talk. I don't mind what she thinks. For the first time in my life, I don't mind what other people think, and it is like a great weight lifted and thrown away to write that down and then read it. I don't mind what other people think. It is the biggest surprise of all. For until today, I think I have minded what other people think of me more than anything else. Perhaps because no one ever said that it didn't matter. Not even Sam, who is good, and goes by his own rules. And certainly at home, other people's views were always terribly important. Even I was explained away, just to make sure everyone knew; then they weren't really responsible for anything I might do. It wasn't their fault. They'd done their best for me. They had, too. They were always good to me. I lived with them for ten years and never once in all that time did they hit me, or speak harshly to me or in any way make me feel a nuisance. It was just that they never became any more than 'they' to me. I called them Mother and Dad, but in my mind they were always 'they'. Even now as I sit here, miles away from them, many months since I have seen them, in a seedy house in London, in a room they would despise, with a baby, without Sam, I still feel nothing for them. Nothing. They are grey figures in the background. Even Sam seems unimportant at this moment. All that matters is the baby; its harsh small breathing and that it depends on me for life.

I remember the journey in the car quite well. I was ten. The past behind me was a blur of children's homes, kindly people, temporary foster homes, a vague memory of my father, bewildered and grey, and my mother dying in hospital. I can write this too, and feel nothing. It is all so long ago. But the feeling of desolation which had almost drowned me in the car, still comes back to me.

It was an ordinary car, grey with red leather upholstery, which was cracked and worn. In the back were all kinds of oddments; gloves, a briefcase, an old gaberdine coat with oil on it, a packet of biscuits, my suitcase and a box of paper handkerchiefs, the flotsam of a busy woman who spent too much time in a car, and on other people's troubles. She was kind. I can't remember what she looked like, but she was like all the others — kind, soft-spoken, patient and distant. How could she be anything else with a job like this — driving a weeping child through the dirty city streets. It was raining as it can rain only in Manchester, a steady stream of yellow mud, battering against the windscreen, clamouring to get in, streaming in despair round the rubber edges as the glass rejected it. I stared at the windscreen-wipers flicking over and back, over and back, until the tears dried in my eyes and could no longer fall.

'Soon there,' she said cheerfully. 'What a day!'

I said nothing, and I think she was pleased that I had stopped crying. I clung to the little bag I had been given with my night things in it.

'Am I going to stay at this place?' I asked. 'Really stay?'

'Yes, dear,' she said. 'You won't have to move around any more. And I'll be coming to see you whenever you want.'

'And I'll go to school here?' I persisted. We had already talked about this but I wanted to hear it again. Again and again.

'Yes, dear.'

I did not say anything more. I should have been pleased. I was going to stay in one place. My father would be able to come and see me. I was going to live in a house, in a family, like everyone else, and go to school. No more 'homes'; huge buildings where everyone was always waiting for someone or something — for Mum to come out of hospital, for Mum to come back again after she'd just 'gone away', for Dad to come out of prison, for the family to get a house. No more sleeping in large rooms with other girls. No more eating in dining-halls like a school. No more sitting round the television as if you were in a cinema, with people all round you. I was going to be boarded out in a proper house, with a proper family. I had longed for it enough.

And yet now it was actually happening, I could feel myself sinking into a black pit again. I swallowed and glared at the windscreen wipers again. It worked. When we drove up outside the house, my eyes were quite dry, and although my whole neck ached, I knew I would manage.

'Come on, then,' she said. 'You take your little bag, and I'll take the suitcase.'

She dragged the case from the back of the car and shooed me up the path. I rang the bell. The door opened almost at once, and there was Mother, grey and plump and smiling, and the smell of newly-baked cakes washed over us as we stood in the grey on the doorstep.

'Well, here you are at last,' she said, clasping my shoulders with her two hands and giving

9

me a little squeeze. 'Come on in out of the cold, and let's shut the door.'

She bustled. She bustled into the hall, shut the door, helped take my coat off, pushed the suitcase into a corner, hung things up, all the time talking about the weather, the winter, the cold, the difficulties about drying the washing and so on. I was grateful. I did not have to say anything. She did not look at me until we had sat down at the table for a cup of tea and one of those cakes she had just made. Every time I think of Mother, I remember the smell of home-made cakes. They were so good, but they choked me. All I could do was to stare at Mother and the woman who had driven me there. They talked, but I did not hear what they said. I was overcome with a terrible weariness, and it was as much as I could do to keep my eyes open. I don't remember much more about that first day. I suppose I went straight to bed when the woman with the car had gone. I did not see Dad or Sam until the next day anyhow.

It is only now I realize how difficult I must have been at first. I was not unhappy. But I gave nothing. I did not know, of course, that I had anything to give. No one told me. I was glad to be there, and accepted my good fortune by being as little trouble as possible. It was not

difficult. Dad was a kindly person too. He and
Mother had married late and Sam was their
only child. He was fourteen when I went there,
a large untidy schoolboy, with dark hairs on
his chin and upper lip and a shy, gruff manner.
I worshipped him from the very first day. He
came rushing into the kitchen, throwing his
cap and satchel on to the floor, and when he
saw me, he stopped in confusion and blushed,
the spots on his chin glaring red. He looked at
his mother and then back at me.

'Hullo,' he said.

'This is Jo,' said Mother. 'Pick up your
satchel and go and wipe your shoes; just look
at them. I suppose there's mud all over the hall
too. I must have told you a thousand times
now. Will you ever learn?'

She said it in a kindly tolerant way. Not
sharply. In fact in the way she treated us all,
Sam, Dad and me, always, as if we were all
muddy school children, who always forgot to
wipe our shoes on the mat.

Sam stumbled good-naturedly out of the
kitchen again, and I heard him scrabbling
about in the hall. When he came back again,
his hair was brushed and he was grinning
cheerfully. I soon learned that Mother set great
store by little things like wiping your feet,
brushing your hair, coming in by the front

door, not the back, not shouting in the garden and always saying good-morning to the trades-men.

Dad came back at six o'clock and we all had tea together. High tea, with a proper cooked course and cakes and tea afterwards. We never had tea until Dad was back. He was a big man, and worked in the tax office in the city. That first evening he put his hand on my head and said:

'So this is Jo, is it? What a wee scrap of a thing you are. Mother'll soon feed you up, won't you Mother?'

He sat down at the table and Mother fetched plates and dishes and made a great fuss of him. I can remember the sense of safety I felt that first day. Everything was safe here. Mother was nothing like the little I could remember of my own mother; a misty, wraith-like figure, so often ill, and so young-looking. And my father was hardly ever at home — there seemed to be no connection between him and this solid, elderly man sitting comfortably at the table, as if he did the same thing at the same time every day of his life. Which indeed he did. Nothing could possibly upset them, I felt, and they had included me in their circle just like that. I know now that the rush of warmth that filled me must have been gratitude, which I could not possibly express, but it was as strong and memorable as the misery I had felt in the car the day before. I spoke for the first time.

'You're nice, like Father Christmas.'

They all laughed and Mother went quite pink. She picked up plates and clattered with knives and forks and said:

'You're right, Jo dear. He *is* nice. Now, Samuel Bent, just you take those elbows off the table and learn a thing or two from your father.'

Sam hurriedly sat up. Whenever Mother had a homily for him, she called him Samuel Bent. 'Samuel Bent, whose socks are these lying about in the bathroom? Come here, young Samuel Bent, and pick these things up.' Otherwise she just called him Sam.

I don't think I spoke again that day. In fact Mother once told me many years later that I did not say anything for about a week, and that she began to wonder whether I were deeply miserable. I laughed at the time and told her that I had not been at all miserable, and had certainly not been silent for any other reason than that caused by a great contentment, which seemed to cover me completely. Perhaps I thought that if I said anything it might all crack and break apart. When I lay in bed at night at that time, I used to think of the Bent family as a huge cotton-wool tent, a bell-shaped tent in which we all lived. And my worst dreams were when a knife would slice a wide crack down the side of the bell and let things in. I never saw what the things that got in were, as I always woke up just as I was forced to turn round and look. But I knew they were evil and had come for me, not for Sam, or his mother and father.

For the next five years, I was for the first time in my life a part of an ordinary family. I was part of something, and the orderly routine of everyday living, so dull perhaps from the outside, smoothed out the jagged pieces which had pricked me and torn at me for so long. I did well at school and went to the grammar school for girls. Sam helped me. He wanted to go to college and he worked hard at his exams night after night, all through the term. To me, he was almost a man, a younger version of Dad, young Samuel Bent, years and years older than me, but someone who would play with me sometimes, as well as help me with home-work.

We usually did our homework in the front room, or else we sat in the kitchen after tea, while Mother and Dad went into the front room. But the television was in the kitchen, so more often than not we went into the front room.

Once, when we had finished earlier than usual, Sam suddenly said:

'Do you miss your mother?'

It came as a shock to me to find that I could hardly remember my real mother at all.

'Sometimes.'

'But Mother's good to you.'

'Of course she is. That's different. She's your mother. Not mine.'

'I can't think what it'd be like,' he said, 'not having a mother.'

'It's a bit as if you always felt you'd done something wrong,' I said suddenly. I was startled by my own words, which had come out quite on their own.

'Wrong?' said Sam. 'How could it be your fault that your mother was ill so much?'

'I don't know. I know it's silly. But it's like that sometimes. As if all the fuss and bother and my father going away and all that, was my fault.'

'But you know it wasn't your fault.'

'Oh, yes,' I said. 'I know all right. But what's the use of knowing when you still feel the same. I sometimes wonder if my father can't bear to come and see me for the same reason.'

'What do you mean?' said Sam. 'He doesn't come because he thinks it was *your* fault, or all *his* fault?'

'I don't know really. Mine, I suppose. I know it's silly. But it doesn't seem to help to know it's silly either.'

I shifted my school books into a heap and started shuffling papers together. I put the books into my satchel. It was the first time I had ever talked about anything beyond school and homework and home to Sam. I looked at him. In a way, I looked at him for the first time. He was seventeen now, and shaved, and most of his spots had gone. I looked at his wide forehead and the great bush of hair he had brushed back from it. I looked at his nose, so like his father's, his broad chin and sturdy neck. His mouth was wide too, rather loose, with a thick lower lip which he was always sticking out and folding back when he was stuck with his work. I suddenly saw his face as a whole. His eyes were very dark brown, like his father's too, and they were looking straight back at me. For a moment, a very short, flickering moment, we just stared at each other, and I wondered if he were looking at me for the first time, and seeing me for the first time too. Then he grinned in his usual way and said:

'You've got ink on your nose.'

16

'Beast!'

He jumped up and avoided my sudden attack.

'Hey! Help! I'm being attacked! Oh, Mother, where are you? Your one and only beloved son is in danger!'

Then we put all our books away and went into the other room. It was an evening like any other evening. I had not seen my own father for two years, and already he was a stranger, a pleasant stranger who once or twice had come to take me out to a stiff and awkward tea at a café. I suppose I had changed a lot too. At thirteen I was still small, but I had grown in other ways. I had filled out and was horribly conscious of my breasts and changing figure. The girls at school had taught me how to do my hair in a different way too, and although Mother frowned a bit at what she called my 'fancies', secretly I used to look in the mirror at myself and wonder at what I saw.

I could never connect the solemn face, the round cheeks and slow grey eyes that I saw in the mirror with the girl I knew to be me. It didn't matter whether I were angry or sad or happy or just ordinary, whether my mind were in a whirl of dismay and indecision, or a complete blank, the girl in the mirror always looked the same. She reflected nothing. Sometimes

17

when I sat at the table in the front room talking to Sam, I would suddenly think: Does he see now what I see in the mirror? Or am I someone different in someone else's eyes? And then we would talk about the Napoleonic Wars or Specific Heats, and I would forget.

I remember it as a time of peace.

The baby stirred and made small signs of distress. Before they could become cries, I had lifted him up and was holding him in my arms. His eyes opened and then closed again as they met the light. He was very young — no more than a month or so old — and was no bigger than a doll. He opened his eyes again and looked at me. He turned his head towards me and I knew he was seeking my breast. I took the bottle from under the tea-cosy and pushed the nipple into his mouth. He sucked at it quickly at first, and then, his first hunger satisfied, with an even, breathing rhythm.

I watched him, his cheek to my breast, his face working and his fingers clenching and unclenching. My arm fitted in the curve round the bundle that was him, just as if it had been made just for this purpose and no other. A calm contentment filled me. I looked round the room and even its shabby dreariness was a comfort to me. The bed, the chair, the small table and the ugly wardrobe, they all contained us. The curtains, thick and lined and obviously handed down from some grand drawing-room, shut out the world and kept us inside our world. I could stay here for ever.

When I at last got back into bed and lay in the dark, listening to the baby's snuffling, my thoughts began to crowd in on me, demanding, asking, proposing, suggesting. But I pushed them away. I would not try. I would not think. I was here with the baby and that was enough. I fell asleep at last. I woke intermittently throughout the night and listened to that small rasping breathing.

2

This morning when I woke up, the room was quite familiar to me. I knew exactly where I was at once. No fumbling in my head, no quick exchange of possibilities. I was in my room, lying in bed, staring at the dirty wallpaper and the bright square patch where there had once been a picture. The wardrobe was too close to the bed, the table was covered with the baby's oddments, the chair was buried under my clothes. The baby was quiet.

I got up, leaned over to look at him, and then went back to heat his milk on the gas ring. I slipped the bottle inside the tea-cosy again and went back to bed. It was early. Not yet seven, but even so, I could hear the trembling roar which is London's traffic, there all the time, wherever you live. It sounded a long way away. It was a brightish morning with no sun.

As I lay there, I thought about my room at

home; the little bedroom with its pink walls and flowered curtains. Mother had had it done up for me when I passed my exams. The curtains matched the coverlet and Dad had made a desk out of the corner of the room, with a bookcase running along the window. The linoleum was polished and there was a thick red rug on the floor. It was mine. My very own room. I could go to it when I liked, and stay there when I liked. At first I could hardly contain my delight and used to sit there, hour after hour, just looking round, as happy as a squirrel in a hole in a tree. But then Sam went away and things changed.

The baby was awake. At first I did not notice, as he was quite silent. But then I saw his eyes were open, just like slits, and he was pushing his fist of fingers into his mouth. I picked him up and changed his clothes and then took him back to bed with me, to give him his morning bottle. As he sucked away placidly, I had to think. I would have to get more milk, to wash his things out, to take him out for a walk, to go outside my room. I would have to stop not thinking. I could no longer just deliberately not think about things until after they had happened. As I had with Sam.

It was the summer holidays after our exams.

Sam had left school and was off to college in the autumn. I was to start in the sixth form at the same time. We took a bus out of the city, and spent the day walking on the moors. The bus rumbled through the blackened, filthy streets, past the great glass palaces which were shooting up all round, with the crumbling remnants of slums still sitting like weeds at their feet. Then the bus slowly left the city behind as it began to touch on the stone villages outside. We got out and humped our small haversacks and set off towards the hills. Sam was a member of the climbing club and he often took me on these rambles. He knew the hills. So I just followed.

For a long while we just trudged over the rough grass without saying anything. When we got to the top of the first hill and had started along the ridge, the wind stinging our faces and the sun feeling that much nearer, Sam striding ahead of me, not too fast, as he knew I could not always keep up with him, then the feeling of release began to come over me. It had happened before, once or twice. As if the whole of me were tied together by a complicated series of knots and bows and laces, each one of which was vital to the whole. And then they would loosen slightly, all at once, and I would feel as if I were a totally different person. And I could stand outside myself and look in at myself.

I must have let out a sigh of contentment, or made some other sound, because Sam turned round and said:

'Are you all right? Shall we stop for a while?'

'Oh, Sam,' I said. 'Isn't it wonderful to be up here, where there's no one else. Not a single living creature. Just look.'

I swept my arm right round to take in the knobbly hills, the grey stone walls, the distant haze and the woods the other side of the valley.

'I could live here,' I went on. 'Right up here, away from the city, away from everyone.'

Sam looked at me.

'You can't live without people,' he said. 'Everyone has to have someone else. Someone to live for. Or with. Or through.'

'I wouldn't,' I said. 'I could live alone. I'd grow my own food, milk my own cow, dig my own land.'

'What for?'

'What for? Why, to keep alive, of course.'

'And is just keeping alive enough?' he said.

That was like Sam. He did not talk very much, but he was thoughtful and he always asked questions. Questions which required answers you had to think out. He never pushed his views. But you could almost smell when he was disapproving in some way. His dark eyes went blank, and I used to feel I'd gone wrong and hurried to repair whatever damage I'd done.

'I don't know,' I said.

'Here, let's sit down and have some coffee.'

Sam swung off his haversack and began fumbling for the thermos in it. I sat down and put my chin on my knees, my eyes skimming the distance, but looking at nothing.

Sam handed me some coffee in a plastic mug. It was always he who did things, the practical one. He was the one who saw to it that the thermos was actually in the haversack, who made sure I'd got my bus pass, who found lost things.

'Here, drink this.'

We sipped the coffee in silence for a while. Then Sam said:

'Are you going to be all right when I'm at college?'

He said it diffidently, quietly, as if it were a routine question. We had talked about it before. I knew he was going. I had known for a long time. And there would be the holidays. Long holidays. Mother and Dad would still be there too. But I had not really thought about

24

it. I had not even begun to think about what it would be like without him. I had no other friends at school. I had Mother and Dad and Sam. It was enough. I leaned back and closed my eyes.

'Yes, of course. I'll have lots to do next term, and it'll soon be Christmas.'

I heard a rustle beside me and opened my eyes. Sam had rolled round and was staring at me, a puzzled expression in his eyes.

'Yes,' he said. 'I won't be far away.'

Suddenly he leaned over and kissed me on the cheek. I hardly felt it, and for a moment wondered whether I had dreamt it. It was the first time he had ever touched me deliberately like that. I could feel myself tremble, and I sat up.

'Don't.'

'Why not?'

I did not know why not, but I said again stupidly: 'Don't.'

'Don't you like me any more?'

'Sam! What a question!'

How could I explain? How could I tell him that I did not want anything changed. No one had ever kissed me before — no boy, that is. I did not like boys. Only Sam. And I did not want Sam to become just another boy, a boy-friend, subject to endless talk and references to things I neither knew about, nor especially wanted to know about.

'You aren't my sister, you know,' Sam said at last.

I stared at him. I felt suddenly as if I were on the very edge of a high cliff; as if the next step, the next word, the next move, would bring about an immense catastrophe. What was I doing, sitting here in a stony wilderness, miles from the orderly confines of house and school and Mother and Dad, talking to Sam, who was saying, almost coldly: You're not my sister, you know.

I looked down at my feet, at my scuffed walking shoes and thick socks. I wanted to shout: No! I'm not your sister. I don't want to be your sister either. I just want you there, always. Just there beside me, as you've always been. To pick me up when I fall. To prop me up when I lean. To help me when I'm helpless. To be kind when I'm hurt. To forgive me when I'm unforgivable. To be there, someone I could trust never to go away.

But all I said was: 'No, I'm not. I know.'

Of course, I did not know then what I know now. I did not know that one move on my part might have made all the difference. I did not know that trust involved two people, not just me. Sam did not say anything more. We got up and walked for the rest of the day, walked and walked until we were tired out, and on the journey back to the city we were both silent, from exhaustion more than anything else.

It was not until December that I noticed what was happening. Sam had been away two months. I lost interest in everything to do with school and school work. I, who had before been a conscientious and hard-working pupil, who had really liked reading and learning, who liked books, the feel of them, the smooth paper, the orderly files of knowledge, the satisfaction of solving an intricate problem, the routine simplicity of work to do each evening. Suddenly I could not even read to the end of a page without a conscious effort. It began to show in my marks too. Then one day I was told to go to the headmistress's study.

She was behind her desk as usual, her kindly face screened off behind her glasses, her hair neat and well-kept, her clothes very good but unexciting.

'Jo,' she said. 'Is there anything wrong?'

I shook my head.

'How do you account for this then?' she said, pointing at the mark-sheet in front of her.

'I don't know, Miss Lane,' I said helplessly. 'I find it hard to concentrate.'

'But you never did before. Why now, all of a

sudden?' she said. Her voice was gentle, but determined.

I could find nothing to say. Nothing at all. How could I find an explanation when I had none? Nothing more was said at the time and Miss Lane said she would leave it until the next term. Perhaps after Christmas I would pull up again. She told me to come to her if I were in difficulties at all, that she knew I had a sticky start in life, that she was there to help, not to scold, that I was a promising pupil, and her voice drifted away out of earshot. She must have seen that she was not making an impression on me, because she sent me away.

I did not pull round. Christmas came and went and at the end of the next term I left school. Mother was upset and went to see Miss Lane, but I was definite for once.

'I want to get a job, Mother,' I said, when she came back. 'I'll never get to college like Sam. And I might as well start now.'

Mother looked troubled. I think she knew something was wrong, but she did not know what. She had felt helpless when talking to Miss Lane, and now she felt helpless talking to me.

'All right, dear,' she said in the end. 'We must see what we can find for you. But I hope you don't regret it.'

'I won't. I'm sure I won't,' I said, and at the time I was absolutely certain that was true. I am still certain that I should never have been able to go on at school. It is about the only thing I've been certain about ever since. Except about the baby.

I carried the baby downstairs and put him into the pram, carry-cot and all. He lay there wide awake and stared at me while I put my coat on. Mrs. Staines came out of her room at the back and said good-morning to me. I said good-morning and began to push the pram out of the front door.

'Going out?'

I turned and said:

'Yes, I'll be back soon.'

She stood there at the back of the dark and grimy hall, her arms folded under her bosom and her chin lowered. Even in the half-light, she looked dirty, and the apron below her folded arms was filthy. Her hair fell in wisps round her face, and her small eyes never left my face. She knows, I thought. She knows all about me. She is just standing there, so that I shall know that she knows. My heart began to thump again as I turned back to the pram. I had thought to ask her where the nearest dairy was, but I changed my mind. The sight of the woman filled me with such revulsion, that I wanted nothing from her. She had had the rent for two weeks in advance, so she could not complain. I pushed the pram down the crumbling steps and turned it towards the noise of the traffic. I felt very upset and my face was burning.

I soon came to a small row of shops. I parked the pram outside and went into the first one. There were several other people in there, but they took no notice of me. I waited for my turn and then asked for a pint of milk, some butter and some cheese. The girl behind the counter never even glanced at me, so by the time I had tucked the things away in the bottom of the pram, I was feeling better. I bought a few more oddments, and then started walking back. At first I thought I would go straight back, but then the picture of Mrs. Staines standing in the hall, looking at me like that, her arms across her grubby belly, and suspicion and fear in her eyes, held me back. It was a mildish morning, so I just pushed the pram aimlessly round the streets for an hour. The baby soon fell asleep.

I felt light-headed and free. I walked and pushed and felt complete. I smiled at other pram-pushers as they went by, complete strangers, and I was warmed by the way they smiled back at me. Now I belonged to the great clan of those who pushed prams and who liked to think themselves makers of men. I knew I was cheating, but somehow it did not matter that morning. I went back to my room.

3

I have had the baby two days now, and already I feel as if I had never been without him. The routine of looking after him seems quite simple, and I am surprised how good he is. He hardly ever cries, and when he does, I only have to pick him up and talk to him and he quietens. He seems to look at me as if to say: I'm safe now. This feeling of safety is something which I've thought about a great deal. To me, it is almost a physical feeling, a box feeling, a feeling of being enclosed. As long as I have walls or something round me, I am all right. As long as one side is open, or there is nothing behind my back, then I am at once uneasy. Perhaps that is why I like this awful room. It is the only one, and all I have is in it. I can close it up and stay inside it. Perhaps that is why I did not really ever like my first job. I never felt safe for one moment.

The woman in the employment agency was very kind. She asked me to sit down and then shuffled round in the drawer, and only when she had a form on her desk in front of her and had extracted a pen from her bag, did she begin to speak, thus giving me time to collect myself and feel calmer.

'Let's fill in all these tedious details first, shall we?' she said, 'and then we can talk about jobs.'

So she took down my name and address, asked about my foster parents, what I'd done at school, and my exam results. Then she said:

'What would you like to do most?'

'I don't know,' I said, and as I said it, I remembered how many times I had said those very words during the last few months. 'But I think I'd like an office job.'

'Of course,' she said, 'if you want a good office job, you need shorthand and typing, but I have some routine filing-clerk jobs you could do, and then you could learn shorthand and typing in the evenings, couldn't you?'

'I suppose so,' I said.

'You can do that at the evening institute or the commercial school in Beeston Road,' she said briskly.

'Yes,' I said, and I could hear the dullness in my own voice. But I could not undo the impression I had made. I could see myself as she saw me, a not unattractive girl in a pleated skirt and a blue jersey, sitting slumped in a chair, apparently taking no interest in her efforts to interest me. I tried to jerk myself into some kind of aliveness and I smiled at her.

'I should like to try, anyhow,' I said.

She looked at me for a moment and then she said slowly :

'You seem rather unhappy about this. Can I help in any way? Is there anything I can do?'

I was taken unaware by this unexpected kindness, especially when I knew I had not been very helpful. For a moment I felt tears rising in my eyes. But I managed to keep them down. Whatever had I got to cry about? I wanted a job, didn't I? And here was someone trying to help me. I pulled myself together and asked for details.

I began at the Health Office the following week. I remember starting off for work at eight in the morning for the first time. I caught the bus and sat with other girls sleepily staring out of the steamy windows as the trauma of night still lay on them. It was only a short distance to walk from the bus stop. I had arrived early and there was only one other girl there when I got into the building. I did not recog-

nize her, as there had been so many girls bust-
ling round on the day I had gone for interview,
that I had felt confused. This girl was in the
hall of the building when I arrived. She turned
round and looked at me when I came in.

'Hullo, a new face. You coming to work
here?'

'Yes.'

'Must be nuts,' she said briefly. 'Coming to a
dump like this. Come on, I'll show you where
we put our things.'

I followed her upstairs and stared at her
stockings and sharp-heeled shoes as we went up
two flights of grimy, uncarpeted wooden stairs.
The girl was dressed in the flashy way that
Mother always spoke sharply about, her coat
short and low-waisted, if a flimsy strip of
material slung loosely across her back, low
down, could be called waisted at all. Her hair
was elaborately piled up on her head and her
face was very pale. When we got to the top,
she turned round and I could see that it was
make-up on her face, thick, caked make-up,
which hid her natural high colour, and that
her pallor was accentuated by thick black
lines round her eyes. I felt very young and
shabby.

'This is where we keep our coats and things,'
she said, as she walked into a room full of pegs

35

and mirrors and wash-basins. 'Female staff room, it's called, but we call it the bog. You can always escape into here when you can't stand the old hag any longer.'

I wondered who the old hag was, but I didn't ask. I hung my coat up, pulled a comb through my hair and waited for the other girl. She was arranging her already perfect hair, patting it down with the palm of her hand. Then she licked her finger and wiped away a little smudge from the corner of her eye. Now she had her coat off, I could see her very short skirt and the frilly blouse she was wearing under a thick cardigan, which hung almost to the hem of her skirt. I looked up to see her eyes looking at me from the mirror.

'First job?' she said, as she carefully applied her lipstick.

I nodded.

'I know how you're feeling. I've been here two years now. Can't think how I've stuck it. But the girls are all right. And it's regular.'

She opened her eyes wide and took a last look at herself. Then she turned to me and added:

'Anyhow, the first week's always perfectly bloody. Here are the others coming now.'

Before I could say anything at all, the room seemed to be full of brightly dressed, chattering girls. They were friendly and cheerful and their language would have made Mother's hair stand on end. It startled me a bit too.

The girl I had met when I had first come in was put in charge of me for the first day. Shirley her name was. 'But call me Shirl — everybody does,' she said. 'What's yours?'

'Joanna,' I said 'Joanna — but most people call me Jo.'

'Jo it is then. Well, come on Jo, and I'll show you the great mysteries of the filing cards in Her Majesty's blooming Health Service. It's just about the dullest job on earth, but if you make a mistake now and again, at least it makes a change. Something to get excited about. At least, the old hag gets excited.'

I spent the day learning to do what Shirley had done for two years. It was horribly simple. Cards came in by the morning post and some had to be filed, some changed and returned, some, from the people who had died, put in the 'mortuary' file. Anything that was the slightest bit complicated was dealt with by one of the senior girls. 'The old hag', a middle-aged woman with a sour expression, was in charge of all the filing clerks, female, unskilled. By the end of the morning, I knew what to do. By the end of the first day, I could do it reasonably quickly. By the end of my first week, I could do it in my sleep. Sometimes there were rushes and we were kept busy, but mostly there was not enough to do. I made tea, fetched and carried, idled at my desk, talked to Shirl, who was knitting a sweater for her boy-friend, and occasionally I escaped into the bog, which I never learned to call the bog, just to get away from the chatter of a room full of bored girls.

There must have been twenty of us all together, but I never got to know any of them really well. Only Shirley, who treated me like a backward child, offering me advice on how to dress, how to get a date, which seats were best for a snuggle in the cinema, where to get the cheapest make-up, and what not to eat if I wanted to keep my figure.

'Not that you have to worry,' she said, eyeing me critically. 'You're the sort that doesn't fatten. Lucky devil. Not for you the horrible agonies of starvation.'

I smiled at her wild language. Starvation! Shirley had fits of conscience about her waistline, and would eat nothing at midday for days on end. Then she would not endure it any longer, and would stuff herself with cream cakes and sweets and biscuits at every moment of the day, all the time sighing for the tightness of the waistband on her skirt and bemoaning her sweet tooth. After weeks of unrestrained eating whenever she felt hungry, she would suddenly confide in me one morning that Reg had said she was filling out a bit. Reg was Shirl's 'steady' and had been for three years now. Everything circled round Reg and what he thought and what he didn't think ought to.

'It gave me quite a turn when he said that,' she said, returning to the subject of her waistline. 'Filling out! I like that. Just as if I were a goose being fattened up for Christmas, or something. So no lunch this week. He says he'll not marry me if I get like my Mum.'

She laughed as she said it. She knew he did not mean it. She and Reg had everything planned out to the last stool in their kitchen, the number of children they were going to have, the colour of the front curtains, and where they were going to retire when Reg was sixty-five. They had even started saving for a house, and would spend their weekends looking at empty houses all over the city. They knew exactly what they wanted and had not yet found it. A nice little house, on the outskirts, not council, but not in a terrace. And they were prepared to wait for it.

'Reg isn't in no hurry and neither am I,' she said one day, as we were sitting in the bog

39

together, away from the old hag's wrath. 'He knows what's what too, does Reg. He's not one to let you down and land you with a brat either.'

'What do you mean?'

'Well, he learned all that in the army. The army has its uses. He wouldn't have known otherwise, he says. But the boys in the army taught him a thing or two.'

'What about?'

She looked at me sharply, and then looked away again. Then she said straight:

'Haven't you ever been with a boy?'

'Been with a boy? What do you mean?'

'Slept with him, silly. You know — the old bit of sex in bed.'

'No.'

I longed to ask her. To find out something. Anything. But she chattered on and I did not have the courage. I felt young and horribly inexperienced beside her cheerful nonchalance.

'Oh, it makes all the difference. Keeps old Reg happy too. And me too for that matter. Can't say I was born to be virtuous. Not me. 'Course, it's a bit different for men. But all the same, I must say I like it. Makes you sort of glow, and of course Reg is good at it. Got a lot of experience, he says. I crown him when he says that, and then he says he learned it all from me. Then I crown him for that too. And then we set to and have another struggle. He's a one, he is.'

She spoke with a kind of bold pride, as if Reg's prowess were a match for her own receptivity. I envied her her assurance and gaiety and her unwavering certainty. I knew that she was not all that she should have been, and I knew Mother would have had a fit if she had heard her talking like this. But I stuck the job for two months largely because of her. I hung on her every word and tried to imagine myself in her world, until she began to notice.

'Here, Jo, stop gawping at me like that. I talk too much. You should be getting yourself a boy, not listening to me gabbling away like that.'

'Why should I?' I said.

'We - ell. I dunno. It's not healthy. I suppose I should keep my big mouth shut. Haven't you got a boy-friend?'

'Only Sam.'

'Who's he?'

I told her. She looked at me, and I think she was just about to open her mouth and ask some questions about him and me, and then suddenly she shut it again and said nothing. If I had chosen that moment to ask her, perhaps things would have been different. Then they found just the house they wanted and within a month they were married. I found to my surprise that I did not really know any of the other girls at all, and suddenly the job was terrible, so boring I could hardly get through the day. I left it in July, the same week that Sam came back after his first year's exams were over.

I hadn't seen him for three months. Mother got his room all ready in the morning and sent me out to do the shopping. He was coming on the midday train. When I got back from the shops, Mother had a cup of coffee on the kitchen table and we sat down together.

'Are you going to meet Sam?' she asked.

I nodded, trying to look calm about it, but Mother saw through me.

'You're fond of Sam, aren't you?'

'Of course.'

'He's a good boy, Sam.'

'I know.'

'He'll be pleased to be met.'

I looked at her calm, plump face, the pale eyes and smooth old-fashioned hair. She was looking at me in the way she has always looked at me, her eyes unwavering and seeing only what is on top. For a moment, I thought that perhaps this was the moment when I could really break through and talk to her about Sam, about how I never really thought about anyone else at all, about what Sam might or might not think about me, about things that were personal, delicate and only just touchable.

'Mind you don't forget your bus fare.'

The moment vanished, as always. I got my bag and left the house with a heavy heart. Why could I never reach anyone? Why was I always on the very edge of other people? Why did I always seem to be the one who stood on the edge of the crowd and experienced only the thinned-out dullness of passed-on information?

When I took the baby out for a walk in the afternoon, I had a shock. As I swung the pram round the corner into the park gates, I almost ran into a policeman. He stepped hastily to one side and I stopped with a jerk. Then he smiled at me and said: 'Sorry, madam.' I stood absolutely still and stared in terror. How could he have known I was coming just at that moment? How had he found out? I could feel the sweat trickling down my back and my throat felt quite dry and stiff.

Then he waved his arm and said: 'Carry on,' and my legs walked on. I walked faster and faster and slowly I felt myself coming to life again. How stupid of me. Of course he did not

43

know. I had only imagined that he had looked at me strangely.

After an hour in the park, I went back to my room.

4

I had a bad night. I dreamed horrible things and could not remember them when I woke up. And each time I woke up, it was so quiet, I was sure the baby was dead. I kept getting out of bed to see if he was all right, which of course, he was. He was sleeping so soundly, he hardly made a sound.

But I heard all the other sounds. The creak of the bed. The slamming of car doors. The traffic. Someone running down the street. A far distant klaxon wailing its horrible up-and-down wail until it faded away. I lay there willing myself to go to sleep, willing myself not to think about Sam. But it always came back to him. Everything in the end came back to him.

The first summer when Sam came back from college was a wonderful one. The weather stayed fine for what seemed like weeks on end,

and all four of us went to the Welsh coast for a
week's holiday. I had never been to Wales
before and I was surprised that such lovely
wild country, such miles of it, could be so near
and yet so few people in it. It was softer
country than the hills round Manchester.
Greener and softer.

We walked for miles. We swam in the warm
sea and we messed about on the shore like a
couple of kids. Mother had not mentioned my
giving up the job and neither had Sam said
anything about it. But of course, he could not
very well pretend that it had not happened.

'What are you going to do, Jo?' he said one
day, when we were lying in the sand, doing
nothing in particular. Dad and Mother were
some way away, sitting in deck chairs, snooz-
ing, and Sam and I were lying on our stomachs
on our towels, after bathing.

'What do you mean, do? Now, or next
term?'

'When we get back, of course,' said Sam, a
little impatiently. 'What kind of job are you
going to try for? Aren't you going to try to get
a training of some sort?'

'I must, I suppose,' I said. 'But I don't
want to think about it now. Not now. It can
wait.'

Sam was silent for so long that I looked up

to see if he had fallen asleep. But he hadn't. He had propped himself up on one elbow and was looking at me steadily.

'I think you ought to,' he said. 'If you just idle about at home, you'll get fat and never want to do anything.'

'I won't get fat,' I said. 'Shirl says I'm not the sort.'

I had told Sam about Shirl and Reg — at least not about everything, but about how funny she was, and how she had cheered me up at work.

'I don't care what Shirl says,' Sam said now. 'It's about time you listened to me. Come on, lazy, get up and let's walk up on to the dunes.'

He slapped my behind and jumped up and ran away. Furious, I jumped up and ran after him. But, of course, he was much too fast for me and was sitting on the top of a dune waiting for me as I trudged up the slope, my feet slipping in the loose sand, and myself puffing and blowing like a grampus. Sam put out a hand and hauled me up the last bit.

'There you are,' he said. 'Take a last look. I must say we've been lucky. Just look at the sea. It's actually sparkling.'

It was. We just sat there, looking. There were quite a lot of people on the shore, but none up here. It was windy but warm, and the sand trickled through your toes like water.

'Jo,' Sam said suddenly. 'Will you wait for me until I come out of college?'

I said nothing. I held my breath. Wait for him? What did he mean? I would wait for him for ever. I would do anything he said. Anything.

'Wait for what?' I said, leaving it to him, as usual.

It was very quiet — people on the shore were calling and dancing about as if what was going on up here was nothing. The sand trickled through my toes and I noticed that my feet were brown and very clean indeed, the kind of cleanliness that water and soap never achieves.

'Well,' said Sam. 'You know. We sort of belong, don't we? And now I've been away, I haven't found anyone I want to be with as much as you.'

'Not any of those clever girls?' I said.

'They're not clever; just girls,' he said.

I pushed my foot through the sand.

'I thought you'd find me dull when you came back,' I said. I dug my foot deeper. 'Especially after leaving school and being no good and taking that awful job and then not even making a go of that.'

'Those aren't things that matter ... but ...'

'But what?'

He turned to me and looked at me for the first time since we had begun talking.

'What do you want, Jo?' he said. 'What do you really want? I've often meant to ask you. What are you looking for?'

'I'm not looking for anything,' I said. 'I don't know what I want. I like things as they are. As long as you are around. I want whatever you want.'

'But do you know what I want?'

'No.'

I didn't. I had no idea. And if I were honest with myself, neither did I mind what he wanted, as long as I was included in it.

'But ...'

He did not go on. At the time I hardly noticed, but I remembered later on. I remembered that 'But ...' and, as usual, wished I had said something then — anything. But of course I was too tied up with what I wanted, not what he wanted.

'I've two more years,' he went on. 'Then I should be able to get a decent job and we could ... we could get married.'

'You want that?'

'Of course,' he said. 'As soon as we can. Not like Mother and Dad — I want to be young and have children when I'm young, and enjoy them when I'm young . . .'

He stopped again. We had never talked like this before. He was talking of getting married. Of having a home and children. Of what we would do in two years' time. I felt I ought to be saying something, but there did not seem to be anything to say. It was everything I had ever wanted. Sam and the rest of our lives together. And now he had just said it all, out aloud, on the sands here in Wales, as if it were just a plan for what to do the next day.

'What do you think?' he said.

All this time he had not touched me. We had sat together up there on the dunes, looking out at the sea, just as we had done many times before. But now he put his hand down on mine as it lay there, propping me up in the soft sand, and he began to run his fingers along mine, rubbing the grit into my skin. I felt at peace, as if no one in the whole world could possibly have my good fortune. To speak would spoil everything.

'What do *you* think?' he said again.

'I can't think,' I said at last. 'There's nothing to think about. I want whatever you want.'

We told Mother and Dad that night, over supper. Sam told them. They were pleased, but at the same time hesitant.

'You're very young, both of you,' said Mother.

'We'll wait till I get a job,' said Sam. 'We'll be a lot older then.'

Dad did not say anything, but he smiled at me in that gentle way he had. He always fell in with Mother anyhow, and I think he thought it was nice to have everything in the family, that if Sam married me, in some way he would not be losing Sam — or me, perhaps.

'Are you going to be officially engaged?' asked Mother. 'Or is it going to be unofficial for the time being?'

'What do you think, Jo?' said Sam.

'I'll do whatever you think best,' I said. 'I don't mind either way.'

'Yes, but what do you think yourself?' persisted Sam. There was a trace of impatience in his voice, almost annoyance, and I looked at Mother for a moment. She was frowning slightly.

'Well, don't let's bother about that now,' she said quickly. 'We can decide when we get home.'

So Sam and I were unofficially officially engaged. To me, the next two years were a wonderful time. I even got myself a job, working in a children's day nursery, helping with the children who were left there all day, some babies, some toddlers and a few older children. It was hard work but I liked it and the holidays were quite good, so I could take time off when Sam came back for the vacations. It was in some way like our schooldays again. Sam did a lot of work in the vacations and sometimes he took a holiday job to earn a bit of money. Then he would come and meet me at the end of the day and we would arrive back home together.

The time rushed by and before I could really believe that it had happened the two years had gone by. Sam finished at the college and got himself a job. In London.

'I've found a little flat,' he said. 'It's not bad. Not exactly luxurious, but not too expensive and it's not far from work, so I could walk there in the mornings. That'll save fares.'

I went up to London with him to look at the flat. Some people were still living in it, but he was to have it as soon as they left. He was going to live there straight away and decorate the place right through before we got married.

I wandered round the little flat. It was at the top of a large old-fashioned house, and must have been the servants' bedrooms. The roofs were sloping and there were four rooms, one large living-room, a bedroom, a tiny kitchen and an even tinier bathroom. It was like a doll's house.

'Sam,' I said. 'It's fine. Just what we want. Pity we can't stay here now for ever and ever.'

Sam came up behind me and put his arms round me.

'That's all right with me, if it's all right with you,' he said laughing.

He hugged me tight and did not let me go. I could feel his long strong body up against mine and I liked the feeling. As if his strength made me strong too. I stood quite still and we did not move for a whole five minutes. Sam seemed to be breathing heavily down my neck.

'Jo!' he said, and his voice sounded different. 'Jo, I want you rather badly.'

I could feel myself stiffen. I had not really meant to, but it just happened.

'We'll be married soon, Sam,' I said. 'Let's wait. Don't let's spoil everything now.'

'Spoil?' he said.

I could feel him moving away a little, and at the time I remember I was only relieved.

Sam kissed me lightly on the back of my neck and moved right away. I fiddled with some things in the kitchen and pretended to look at the gas meter under the sink. The atmosphere was strained in some way and I tried to think what I had done wrong. I knew what Sam had wanted. We had never spoken about it. But we both knew. And it was as if by some unspoken agreement, we would leave that until we got married. But sometimes I thought of Shirl and I wished I knew a bit more, that I knew someone I could ask. I was so happy and pleased that Sam had not pestered me that I thought that was what he wanted too. I think it was too. But now I realize that it was not so simple as that.

Sam kissed me goodbye at the station and squeezed my hand.

'See you at our wedding,' he said, as he stood there on the platform below me.

'Only a fortnight,' I said. 'Mother's in a bit of a tizzy, but I think she's enjoying it all.'

I went back to Manchester and Sam stayed on in London. I was busy and Mother was busy and although I missed him, I was certainly not unhappy. Everything seemed to lie in front of us, just waiting for us to pick it up. And I had Sam. Sam was everything. He would look after me and I would do anything to make him happy. He knew that.

The only thing wrong was that I thought that to make a person happy, all you had to do was just to agree. No one had ever told me you had to do something positive sometimes too.

But at that time I did not even know what doing something positive was.

At three o'clock in the morning I got up and made myself a hot drink. I sat on the edge of that horrible bed, sipping at my drink and trying to think. For the first time I tried to think about the future. Not just tomorrow or the next day. But beyond that.

And that was the first time I really understood what I had done. Up until then I had had so much to think about that was close to me, the baby, his food, somewhere to live, looking after him, where to go, what to do next, that everything else had just vanished to somewhere at the back of my mind.

Now it came to the front. Now in the cold dark hours of the morning in this room, which only yesterday I had felt so secure in, as if I could have stayed in it all day and all night for ever and ever — now it was hostile and the walls seemed to close in on me. I wanted to scream, or cry, or something, but I knew I would wake the baby, so I did not.

I looked at him. For the thousandth time, I just stared at him. He was so small and he needed me. He was the first person ever to need me and this seemed to be so important. But now I saw what I had refused to see before.

What I had tucked away, although I knew it to be true, what everyone else knew, what I had blindly, almost madly, ignored.

He wasn't mine.

5

The next morning I had a terrible headache. I
had only slept for about an hour, possibly two,
and had then woken again, afraid that I would
oversleep and not hear the baby. I got up and
got his bottle ready, my head throbbing and
my whole body aching. My eyes felt as if there
were sand behind the lids and it was an effort
to keep them open. I felt dirty and unwashed
and the room looked awful. Really awful.

What should I do?

I fed the baby, changed his clothes and put
him back in the carry-cot. I packed up all the
things I had with me in the suitcase and put
the case down at the end of the bed. I tidied up
the room. I pushed the furniture straight and
dusted over the surfaces of the table and
dressing-table. It looked a bit better but not
much. I cleaned round the cracked basin and
tried to pick up some of the fluff off the floor.
But whatever I did, the room still looked what

it was — a shabbily furnished room, let to anyone who would pay the rent and who was not too fussy.

I thought of the flat, of our furniture and the new things we had had as wedding presents, of the modern cups and saucers we had bought together with the wedding-present money, of the little transistor wireless and the dreadful vase that Dad's elder sister had given us and we did not know what to do with. It was just like the one on the mantelpiece here.

The wedding was a small one. Mother and Dad had asked a few of their friends and Sam had asked some of his, but as we were both of the same family, so to speak, the number of guests was small.

My father came.

I had not seen him for three years now, and in a strange way could hardly remember what he looked like. He came by train as his car was in dock, he said, and Sam and I went to meet him at the station.

He was thinner and his hair had turned quite grey. When he took his hat off, I saw at once that he was going bald, and it came as a shock. I don't know why. I was twenty, so he must be well over forty. But it was a shock all the same.

'Hullo, my boy,' he said, pumping Sam's hand up and down. 'Hullo, dear. How's things?'

We bustled about, Sam taking my father's case and my father protesting that he could perfectly well carry it himself, and that he wasn't dead yet, ha ha, and couldn't we all go and have a drink somewhere first, before we went home to face the crowd.

Sam was a little taken aback, I think, and so was I, but we went out of the station and along the street until we came to a small hotel which Sam knew about. We went into the saloon bar and sat in a corner. I had hardly ever been in a pub before and I felt awkward. But Sam seemed to be quite at ease and it was he who ordered drinks for us all. I had a shandy, which is the only drink I like and Sam had some beer and my father had a double whisky.

'Needed that,' he said, as he tossed down the whisky in one gulp. 'Been a bad week. Well now, and how's my little girl? All ready for the great day? How are you feeling? And you, Sam? What's it like being a working man after all those years over your books? All right, eh?'

My father poked Sam in the ribs and laughed. It was not a very pleasant laugh, and Sam grinned sheepishly, and told him he was glad to be working at last, and that he had got hold of a flat, which we were going straight to after the wedding. My father suddenly looked tired again and was silent for a few moments.

'Sam, my boy,' he said then. 'Get me another drink, will you? I've not been much of a father to Jo here, and it's about time I tried to get to know you both a little better, now you're taking her away from me.'

This seemed a strange way of putting it. Sam was hardly taking me away from him as he had scarcely ever been to see me since I had been in Manchester. But Sam got up and went and fetched another drink for him, and while he was away, my father turned to me.

'Jo, dear,' he said. 'I don't really know what to say, but I ought to say something, I suppose. I hope that you're going to be happy . . . that is I hope you'll be as happy . . . as happy as your mother and I were. Were. Of course, you never really knew her, did you? I keep forgetting. Yes. We were, you know . . .'

'You were what?' asked Sam, putting the whisky down on the table and his change back in his pocket.

'I was just telling Jo that her mother and I were happy once and that I hoped you will be too. It was a long time ago . . . yes . . . she's very like her mother too, you know, very like

60

her. Well, here's to you both. Best of luck and may things work out better for you than they did for me. Yes.'

He sat quite silently for a while and I did not know what to say. He had never spoken of my mother before and now he seemed to be very strange, quite a different person from what I remembered. Sam looked across at me and frowned a little.

'Thank you,' he said simply. 'I hope you'll come and see us when you're in London.'

'Better not, my boy,' said my father. 'Better not. Not a very good idea. Not really my line, visiting. And I'm a very busy man these days. Very busy.'

I did not know what my father did for a living. I knew he travelled a lot by car and that he rarely stayed in one place for long.

'What's wrong with the car?' I said, more for something to say than anything else.

'Pranged it,' he said briefly. 'Smashed it up last week. Cost a fortune to put it right too, it will, and it was my fault so I'll have to pay.'

Then I realized that he was drunk. Not reeling, noisily drunk, like the men you see about on a Saturday night, singing their heads off and generally making a great fuss and noise. But in a glazed way. As if he were rather a long way away from us, and it was with the greatest of difficulty he managed to speak to us. That was why he seemed so strange. At first I was worried — what would Mother and Dad say, and would my father make a scene? Or would he be difficult at the wedding tomorrow? But then I felt sorry for him. I realized that it had been an effort to come at all and perhaps drink was the only way he could find of giving himself the strength to face us all.

Sam seemed to understand and took charge of my father.

When we got home, he got him safely sitting in the living-room and took his case upstairs. I went up too.

Sam looked at me across the bed in the room where my father was to sleep for the night.

'Yes, I know,' I said, before Sam could say anything. 'He's drunk, isn't he?'

Sam nodded.

'What can we do?'

'Nothing, except hope everything will be all right. I'll see to him. Keep him out of the way. He'll be going back after the wedding tomorrow.'

The evening meal went off quite well. My father seeemed to be in a cheerful mood and Mother, who had been fussing round for days getting everything done, had calmed down now there was a stranger in the house. My father talked gaily to her and complimented her on her food, her neat and tidy home, and he talked to Dad about cars and work, as if nothing were wrong at all, After the meal, when we were all in the sitting-room, he pulled an envelope out of his pocket and gave it to Sam.

'My little contribution,' he said. 'Didn't know what you wanted, so thought good old £ s d would be the best. Sorry it's not more.'

Sam took the envelope and opened it. It was a cheque. For fifty pounds. A lot of money for Sam and me.

'Thank you,' Sam said. 'You needn't have been so generous. We can manage. I hope you can spare it.'

'Least I could do,' said my father grandly, waving his arm. 'Least I could do. Buy her something — something nice. I'm handing her over to you now, you know.'

He had handed me over to someone else all his life. Not just now. I saw now quite clearly what I had never really thought out before. My father was a weak man and perhaps my mother, who had been pretty and young when she had died, had been the stronger of the two. And when he had been left with nothing but me, he had taken the easy way out. Let other people decide. And now Sam was taking me over, he was relieved. His last responsibility had gone. I could not be angry.

I remembered telling Sam that I had always felt that it had been my fault that my mother had been ill. Perhaps that's just what my father had thought too? Perhaps it was the truth and he had never been able to forgive me for it. I looked at him now, crumpled up in the arm-chair Dad usually sat in, his suit a little worn, his cuffs a little frayed, his shirt not quite clean and the sad far-away look in his eyes. He did not seem a real person to me at all, least of all my own father. And he was so different from Dad, who was sitting there on an uncomfortable up-right chair, grey and old, neat and spruce, puffing away at his pipe, while Mother fussed round with cups of tea.

'I think I'll go to bed now,' I said, getting up from my chair. 'Good-night, Mother and Dad. Good-night . . .'

I could not call him Father, or Daddy as I called him when I was little. So I quickly leaned down and kissed him on the forehead. He caught hold of my hand and gave it a squeeze. It was the last time he ever touched me, except to hold my arm as he walked up the aisle in the church. And except to say goodbye after the wedding, it was the last time I ever saw him. He was killed in a car smash —

another — about a month after we were married.

The wedding went off without a hitch. It was not an elaborate affair and afterwards we had the reception at home. Mother had arranged everything and some of her friends came in to help hand round the food. There was champagne and a lot of talk and laughter and Dad's friends pecked me on the cheek and tickled my face with their moustaches. I hardly seemed to see Sam, but he was very much there all the time. I had gone through the service in a kind of dream, not a rosy dream of romance, but a kind of calm dream, a little impatient, as if the whole were just something to please Mother and Dad and my father.

On the train, Sam held my hand and we sat without saying anything for a long time. We were both worn out and I slept for a while. When I woke up, Sam looked at me and said:

'Well, Mrs. Bent?'

'Well, Samuel Bent?'

We both laughed.

'Don't you start calling me that,' said Sam, 'or I shall keep looking round to see what I've done wrong.'

'All right,' I said. 'I'll call you whatever you want to be called.'

He glanced at me, the same look he had given me that day when we had told Mother and Dad we wanted to get married, three years ago, almost. But he said nothing. He looked at his watch.

'We'll be there soon.'

Those first few weeks when we were settling into the flat were busy but happy ones. I was full of being the little housewife and running the flat, keeping it clean, polishing and tidying, cleaning the bath, washing Sam's clothes, ironing, cooking, shopping, and loving it. We had two weeks without anything else to do but enjoy ourselves, and then Sam went back to work and we became like hundreds of other young couples, in their first home, with no one to bother about but themselves. Or so I thought.

I discovered what Shirley had meant when she had said, all those years ago, that 'it was different for men'. I had been a little frightened at first over the change that came over Sam when we were in bed together. I knew of course what he wanted. I knew that he had waited all this time and not given way before we were married. And so I knew I should do as he wished. But it wasn't easy. And it wasn't at all as Shirl had implied. I tried hard but I couldn't like it. But everything else was so wonderful, I put it away in my mind and thought that I would get used to it. As long as Sam was happy, that was what mattered.

That evening I made up my mind what I should do. I had had a wretched day and somehow this seemed to have gone over to the baby too. He had whimpered and whimpered and in the end I had taken him out for a long walk until he fell asleep. But when we got back to the room, he would not settle. So I had picked him up and walked up and down the room with him in my arms for a while.

As I walked I thought about what I would have to do. I thought for a moment of getting a job and finding someone to look after the baby. Then I stopped suddenly and pulled myself together. He wasn't mine and I could no longer pretend that I could keep him. I looked down at him. He was quiet now, just lying there in my arms, looking sleepy, and I wondered how I would ever be able to let him go. But I had to. Tomorrow. I would do it tomorrow morning.

I put the baby back in his carry-cot and went down to see Mrs. Staines.

I knocked on the basement door, trembling a little as I did so. I don't know what I had to be afraid of, but I was, and when she came to the

67

door, I could hardly speak.

'Can you spare me a minute, Mrs. Staines?' I said.

She opened the door wider and jerked her head backwards, so I went in. The room was murky and very hot, a huge fire roaring in an old range which ran almost right along one wall. The window was nothing but a slit at the ceiling level and there was a dirty piece of cloth hanging across it. The room was very crowded, a big table in the middle, and a large old sideboard crammed along one wall. There were things all over the place and the mantel-piece above the stove was crowded with objects, vases, clocks, bits of paper, spills, picture postcards and rent books.

'I'll be going tomorrow, Mrs. Staines,' I said. 'I thought I'd better tell you.'

'Oh, yes,' she said, her eyes narrowing. 'That's a bit sudden isn't it. What 'yer going for already? Aren't yer satisfied? I do me best. And the place is clean. Yer can't grumble. It's a big old place to keep all by yerself.'

'It's all right, Mrs. Staines,' I said, feeling desperately tired. 'I'm not grumbling. I just thought I'd tell you, so that you didn't think anything had happened to me.'

'Don't think I can give you any of the rent money back,' she said, her little pig eyes

68

glinting. 'I can't do that. It was in advance and you asked for two weeks now, didn't . . .'

'I don't want the money back,' I said quickly. 'You can keep it.'

As if money made any difference. I began to wish I had not come down now, to wish I'd just left the house without saying anything.

'What're you up to?' the woman was saying. 'You run away, or something, or is that ring there just a bit of show?'

'No,' I said. 'Nothing like that. It's mine all right. And my name *is* Mrs. Bent. I must be going now, in case the baby, my baby. . . .'

'What's his name — or her name?' the woman suddenly asked.

I looked at her. Name? What a question. As if that mattered. He hadn't a name. He was just a baby. A beautiful baby. Someone else's.

'Good-night, Mrs. Staines,' I said. 'I'll be out of the room tomorrow morning.'

I trailed back up the stairs, holding on to the banisters in the gloom. The baby was quite quiet, so I slowly undressed and got into bed. I would go tomorrow morning. Where would I go? Where would I take him? Back to where I had found him? I could not do that. To the police?

Police.

That was what I would have to do. And then

I would have to explain. How could I do that?

I lay in bed thinking, my thoughts running round and round in my head like one of those mice in a wheel, round and round and round, each thought pushing the wheel a bit faster. It seemed hours and hours later that I heard a clock strike two. I seemed to be the only person in the whole of London.

6

I was out of the house by nine o'clock in the morning. Mrs. Staines did not put in an appearance, and I had already packed most of my things in the suitcase the day before.

I walked along the street with the case balanced on the end of the pram. I was not sure where to go, or even in which direction. For a while I just walked, mingling with the people busily crowding along the pavements, just as if I were going somewhere too. I knew I would have to ask someone the way soon, but could not find the courage. It was drizzling slightly and although it was not cold, I kept shivering as if it were. I walked and walked. The baby was quite silent, asleep in the carrycot inside the pram, just as when I had first seen him.

'Excuse me, Madam,' said a voice. 'You dropped this.'

I jumped and stopped. A man was holding out a glove to me. For a moment I stared at it as if it had nothing to do with me at all, and then I pulled myself together, thanked him, and asked him whether he knew where the nearest police station was. He looked at me oddly at first, but then told me to walk on and turn right, and I would find it down that side street.

'Are you all right?' he said. 'Is there anything I can do for you?'

'No, thank you,' I said. 'I'm quite all right. Thank you very much.'

I meant it. In some way he had brought me down to earth, I realized that I had not really spoken to anyone for days, that I had been living in a world of my own thoughts and I had not been thinking about anyone else at all. Now his ordinary voice and ordinary action of picking up my glove, a glove of all things — I could not even remember having any with me at all — seemed to wake me up and make me start behaving like anyone else, asking the way in the street.

'Thank you very much,' I said again.

The police station was an old grey building with a huge door in the front. I had never seen a police station before. At least, I had never really noticed one before, except vaguely from

72

the outside. I peered through the glass doors. Inside there was a largish hall place and a long counter. So I hauled the pram up the three steps and dragged it into this hall.

The policeman at the counter looked up.

'Yes, miss?'

I am not sure why, but when he called me 'Miss' like that, in a kindly, slightly patronizing way, I had a vision of myself standing there, small and insignificant, a girl, a young girl, definitely 'Miss'. Something rose in me and I stood up straighter and said firmly:

'My name is Mrs. Samuel Bent. I've brought back the baby I took.'

He looked straight at me for a moment and then looked across the hall at the pram. Then he nodded slightly towards the pram and said:

'You took, you say?'

'Yes.' I felt surer now I had said it. 'Could I speak to someone about it, please?'

'Just a moment, please, Miss — er Mrs. . . . what did you say your name was?'

'Mrs. Samuel Bent,' I said, and I sounded just like Mother telling someone, me this time, to go and wipe my shoes on the doormat.

The policeman picked up the telephone and muttered into it. Then he listened for a moment and said 'Right' and put down the receiver. I watched his every move. He was a young policeman and made me feel quite old.

'Would you mind coming with me, madam,' he said, terribly politely. 'Inspector Blewit would like a word with you.'

'What about the ...?' I waved my hand towards the pram.

'It'll be all right there,' he said. 'We'll keep an eye on it.'

I picked up my case and followed him. He lifted the flap of the counter and I went through. The flap went down with a bang. We went up some grimy stone stairs, along a corridor and came to an office with a glass pane in the door. The policeman knocked and opened the door at once.

I went in. At a desk sat an older man in ordinary clothes.

He rose, shook my hand and asked me to sit down. Another young policeman was sitting in a chair by his desk, a notebook and pencil in his hand.

'I am Inspector Blewit,' he said when he had sat down again. 'Would you mind telling us again what you have come for?'

It was like a social visit. I felt calm, the panic I had felt in the street slowly fading away as I told this man that I had brought the baby back,

74

the baby I had taken from outside the shop and that I was sorry.

Of course, it took longer that that. He asked me a lot of questions and just where I had taken the baby from, and then he looked in some papers and looked up again.

'He's all right, is he?' he said.

'Who?'

'The baby?'

Then I thought of the baby's mother for the first time — and as the Inspector lifted the receiver again and got put through to a number, I tried to put myself in the position of the person on the other end of the 'phone.

'Mr. Craig? We've found your son ... yes ... yes ... straight away if you like. Yes, he's all right. Quite all right. In fact asleep and well. Yes, tell your wife, but make her stay in bed if she's not well. If you come straight away, you can take him home ...'

The Inspector gave the address on the 'phone and then put the telephone down.

There was a long silence, then he looked up at me and looked down at the papers on his desk again.

'You realize that you will have to stay here for a while,' he said. 'Until we can make further enquiries. Is there anyone you would like to get in touch with?'

I shook my head.

'What about your husband?' he said.

Sam. What would he say? What would he say when a policeman arrived to say his wife was at a strange police station at the other end of London? I shook my head again.

The Inspector muttered something to the young policeman, who got up and went out. A few minutes later he was back with a sheaf of papers in his hand which he put down in front of the Inspector. The Inspector ran his fingers down the list on the top one.

'Bent?' he said. 'Samuel Bent?' Then he read out the address of our flat.

I nodded.

'Your husband has been looking for you,' he said. 'Do you want to see him?'

Of course I wanted to see him. What a question. But would he want to see me? Suddenly I was terribly tired again and could not think any more. Now I had actually come here and done what had to be done, I seemed to be drained of energy, almost incapable of lifting a hand.

I nodded.

'Yes, please.'

'You'd better come with me then,' said the Inspector, rising from his chair.

He took me to a bare, rather cold waiting-room on the same floor. A woman policeman brought me a cup of tea and told me I should not have to wait too long, that they had telephoned my husband and he was coming at once.

I sat on the hard chair and looked up at the high window, facing a wall of another building, so dirty it was almost impossible to see through it. It was a grey day outside and I could hear the shouts and cries of school-children somewhere, let out into the yard to play.

We had both wanted children straight away. Both of us. So I did not even try to get a job when we were first married. Sam earned a good salary and it was plenty for us two. So we said we would start a family straight away.

'There's plenty of room for one baby here,' Sam said, looking round our flat. 'And there's nothing in the lease about *not* having children here, so we could stay here until number two comes along.'

Sam wanted four children. He once told me that he had always wanted four children. His childhood had been a lonely one and he wanted his children to grow up with others, in a family, rubbing along with others. He said he had not known how lonely he had been until I had come to live with them.

It was fine at first. Sam went off to work in the mornings and came back in the evenings, I kept the flat beautifully clean and I did everything, washing, ironing, shopping, decorating and cooking. I had to learn to cook properly and we had a lot of laughs over my less successful efforts. Especially pastry which turned out as hard as rock and cakes which fell flat as a pancake and tasted like sweet rubber.

'You'll be the death of me,' said Sam one day, chewing away at something else that had gone wrong.

But I got better at it, of course. And I took great pride in having everything ready when he got back — the table laid, the supper in the oven, myself neat and tidy and not hot and bothered. I always had it ready, and when he came clumping up the stairs, I would hear him and rush to open the door. He would come into our tiny hall, give me a kiss, take off his coat, go and have a wash and then we would eat our meal together and talk about the day's happenings. It was enough.

I mended his socks, kept his shirts neat and made sure he always had a clean handkerchief. We hardly ever went out in the evenings, except to the cinema now and again, partly because we did not want to much, and partly because we were saving — saving for a bigger flat or even a house, and saving for the things we would need for the baby.

But there was no baby. And Sam began to change. Just a little at first. I did not notice at first, but then I began to see that he was restless sometimes in the evenings.

'Let's go out somewhere,' he would say.

'Oh, no, Sam. It's all right,' I would say. 'I'm quite happy sitting at home if you are.'

'But . . .'

But he did not go on. He would pick up a book and read for a while. Then he would go and make some tea or listen to the wireless, or perhaps slip downstairs to the pub on the corner for an hour, to talk to his friends. I would not go with him, partly because I don't really drink much, and partly because I thought he liked to talk down there without me.

One day, when Sam had just got back and we had sat down for our meal, he suddenly said:

'I had a rise today. Starting next month. Let's go out and celebrate tonight.'

'Oh, that's wonderful, Sam,' I said. 'What shall we do?'

'You say,' said Sam. 'Just say the word, and we'll do it. Go to the Ritz. Walk in the park. A night out at the Palais. Off to the theatre. You say it and I've got it.'

He was in a gay mood. His eyes sparkled and as he sat there across the table, chattering away, I thought how young and handsome he was. Of course he isn't really handsome, but he seemed so alive just then, I could have hugged him.

'I don't mind,' I said. 'You choose.'

His face clouded.

'No,' he said. 'You say, for once.'

'Really, I don't mind, Sam,' I said. 'I'd like to do whatever you want to do.'

'Don't you *see*,' Sam suddenly shouted. 'I want *you* to choose. To decide for *yourself*, not just to do what I want to do.'

It was absolutely quiet in the flat. I sat staring at Sam. He had never spoken to me like that before — ever. In fact I had never heard him shout at anyone before, least of all me. If he had taken a whip and beaten me across the back with it, I couldn't have been more surprised. I opened my mouth to say something, and then closed it again, because I could think of nothing to say.

Sam hunched down in his chair, his face scarlet.

'Sorry,' he said. 'Sorry, Jo, I don't know what . . . I don't know . . .'

We went out and went to the cinema round

the corner. Afterwards we went to the pub and had a drink and then we came back again. I had had a shandy and Sam a whisky.

'Here's to the rise,' he had said, and drank it all down in one go.

But it was awful. Nothing could have been less like a celebration. We were awkward together for the first time. We did not stay long at the pub and went straight to bed when we got home. When I had put the light out and crept down into bed, Sam put his arms round me and whispered in my ear. He was sorry. He was a beast. He hadn't meant anything. He loved me. I touched his cheek and said nothing. It was enough for me to have him there.

After a whole year there was still no sign of a baby. I went to the doctor and Sam did too, but there was nothing wrong with either of us. I began to feel a little desperate at times. Running the flat was easy and I was so practised at it that it now took up very little of my time. It was the one thing I *was* any good at. I went out in the daytime a lot more and wandered round the streets, looking at people, and in the shops, looking for special things for Sam's supper. I always made sure I was back in time to have his supper ready. Everything was just as before, except that it wasn't.

Sam grew silent. I thought at first it was

because he was thinking perhaps we would never have any children. But it wasn't just that. We had been married for two whole years before I discovered it was me.

Sam had brought some drink back with him and he had drunk more than I had ever seen him do before. Then he dropped a dish when we were washing up. I didn't say anything, but just picked up the bits and threw them in the rubbish bin. We sat all evening without saying very much, just the usual things, and Sam was reading, I sewing on some new curtains.

That night Sam made love to me, for the first time for some weeks. I couldn't help minding about the drink a bit, but I didn't say anything, but just lay there letting him do what he wanted. Suddenly he sat up in bed and said angrily:

'I can't. I can't. I bloody well can't.'

'What's the matter, Sam?' I said. 'Can't what?'

He said nothing for a minute. He was breathing heavily and staring down at his own feet under the blankets. Then he seemed to make a huge effort.

'*You've* got to do something too,' he said. 'It's just as if you weren't there at all. Like making love to a corpse!'

I went cold all over.

'But Sam,' I protested. 'You know I love you. You know that.'

'I *know*. Yes, I *know*. You keep saying so, but it doesn't make any bloody difference,' he shouted. 'We're not two lovers. There's just me. And you doing what I want. And I bloody well can't.'

'What do you mean?' I was quite at a loss and thought he must have gone mad or else had drunk much more than I thought. He never usually swore either. It was all so unlike him. The shouting. Even the drinking. He never usually either drank or shouted. I was quite bewildered.

'Don't you *see*.' he said at last, and he sounded desperate, so desperate I was terribly afraid. 'Don't you see that this is for two people, two of us, both of us and if you don't give something it's no good. No good, d'you see. No bloody good and never will be.'

'I'll try, Sam,' I said feebly. 'I'll try to do whatever you want. I always do.'

Sam leaped out of bed as if I'd hit him. Then he turned round and looked down at me. I could just see him from the light from the window and he looked enormous, towering above me.

'I know you do,' he said. And he was quite calm and cold. 'And that's what's wrong.

83

You've never understood. I don't want you to do whatever *I* want. You must do what *you* want too, or I'll break. I can't be you and me all the time. You've got to want something positive too. Not just through me. I can't bear it.'

He started dressing. I just lay there, too stunned to do or say anything. I heard Sam pulling his clothes on and going out into the hall. Then I heard him opening the door and his footsteps fading away down the stairs. I lay there all night, without sleeping.

Sam did not come back. I got up and made some breakfast, but I couldn't eat it. I drank a cup of coffee and then washed up. Then I cleaned the flat automatically, leaving everything in order.

Then I went out.

I walked and walked and walked. I thought about what Sam had said and slowly began to realize that instead of a help and a companion to Sam, I had been a burden. A burden! A great weight on him. I had failed in this too. Slowly my feeling of anger drained out of me. The anger which I had felt when I thought of how much I had done for Sam, how I had looked after him, cooked for him, seen to his clothes and everything else. But then I began, only began to see, that all that was as if nothing, because I could not look after myself. I could not lift a hand without him deciding where I should put it. And when he wanted to make love to me, there I was as usual, always handy, always willing, but giving nothing in return. Offering nothing but a devotion which in the end was beginning to suffocate him.

And children. Perhaps this was why we had not been able to make a child. I looked at the people in the street, the mothers with their children, the prams, the toddlers, the push-chairs and I tried to see what was different about them. They looked just like people any-where to me and even the poorest seemed to have achieved more than I had. If only we'd had a child, then perhaps things would have been different.

If only. If all the ifs and buts could be put together they would stretch a mile. That was when the idea came in a flash. I suppose I was in a state of mind when all ordinary things just don't count. Anyhow, when I saw the pram outside the chemist's shop, at one moment it was just another pram among many others, and the next moment I was pushing it down the street. I had lifted the brake with my foot, as if I had done the same thing twenty times a day for years, and walked away.

I walked for miles. As I did I became quite

clear in the head and practical too. I stopped at a chemist and bought some milk and a bottle, some paper napkins and other small things I knew I should need. I bought a little food for myself and a small case, and walked on. I went through parts of London I had never seen before, miles and miles of streets. I was not hungry, only elated in some way.

I saw a postcard pinned up on the doorpost of a newsagent's. There was a whole row of them, mostly advertising rooms. I went to the first address I saw. It was a large, once handsome house with a high portico up to the front door. But it was shabby and dirty and the plaster was peeling away in great chunks from the walls. I rang the bell.

Mrs. Staines answered the bell. Quite calmly I told her I wanted her room and was prepared to pay in advance. She showed me the room and the whole matter was settled in about ten minutes. I had three pounds left in my bag. I wheeled the pram into the hall, took the carry-cot and baby out of it, and carried them both into my room. There I looked at the baby for the first time.

The door of the waiting-room opened and Sam came in. I was sitting on the other side of the room and when I first saw him, for one brief moment I thought it was Dad. Dad? They must have fetched him down from Manchester, I thought. What a silly thing to do, to upset the old man with what was nothing to do with him really. Then I saw it wasn't Dad at all, but Sam.

His face was lined and drawn and his eyes looked absolutely hollow, sunk deep into his eye-sockets.

He came straight over to me and pulled me up from the chair and put his arms round me. He seemed taller than ever and we just stood there hugging each other and saying nothing, Sam murmuring 'Jo, Jo, Jo,' in my ear.

I was past saying anything, and so pleased that Sam was here that I just clung to him. A slight cough behind us brought us back to reality.

Sam let me go and turned to the policeman.

'All right if we go back now?' he said.

'Yes, sir,' he said. 'We've got your name and address and as long as you guarantee that Mrs. Bent does not go away, that's all right. Of course . . .' he hesitated, '. . . you realize that there'll . . . there may be proceedings. Someone will be coming to see you . . .'

'Yes, yes,' said Sam, almost impatiently. 'But not today. My wife needs some rest and . . .'

'I'm perfectly all right, Sam,' I said. 'If anyone wants to see me, I can see them now. In fact I'd prefer to get it over and done with.'

But they sent us home. Tomorrow would be soon enough. The baby was in his own home. As soon as we got back to the flat, Sam put me to bed and I fell asleep almost at once. But not before I noticed that the flat was quite clean and tidy. Somehow the thought had gone through my head that Sam would have been living through these days like a pig, eating out of tins, and not washing up or anything. But it was not so. Everything was in order.

'You don't even need me here,' I said weakly.

'Don't you ever say that again,' Sam said sternly, 'Mrs. Samuel Bent.'

I fell asleep.

7

So I learned the hard way. I learned what to love a person meant, that it was not just supplying ordinary things like good meals and clean shirts. That a man does not need you as a baby does. A baby can only give blind love and devotion. And I had been like a baby to Sam, dependent on him all the time, just as the baby had been on me. Not just when we had got married, but for years and years, from the very first moment I had laid eyes on him as he had rushed into the kitchen, spotty and grinning, dropping things on the floor right, left and centre.

Of course, I did not realize all this in a blinding flash, like a revelation. It came slowly, as I began to understand, as people began to explain what seemed so simple, but what I had not even begun to grasp before.

So many people.

Sam took a week's leave and stayed with me

all the time. I had to see a doctor and a pro-
bation officer and the police inspector. I had to
sign statements and go back and forth to that
police station. It all went on for days and I
knew the worst that could happen. If the
mother of the baby brought a charge against
me, I should have to go to court and it would
all be in the papers and we would have to face
up to that too. Everyone was very kind to me,
but firm at the same time. I knew what I had
done. I should have to take the consequences.
But the worst of it was that Sam would have to
take them too.

I went to see the baby's mother. Not just like
that. The doctor asked me if I would like to.
And of course, she was asked too. I could not
make up my mind. But I did in the end. Make
up my mind.

They lived in an ordinary little house in a
street not far away from the chemist's shop. I
went by myself.

I rang the bell. I was horribly nervous and
tried to think of something to say first, but the
door opened before I had thought of anything.
She was a young woman, not much older than
me. She looked at me for a moment and then
she said:

'Are you Mrs. Bent?'

I nodded and when she opened the door

wider, I stepped inside the hall. We went into their sitting-room at the back of the house, and there through the window, I saw the pram out in the garden. I looked at the woman and then away again.

'I'm sorry,' I said foolishly. 'I didn't mean . . .'

Her face softened a little. It had been hard at first, as if she were afraid of me, as if she had been afraid I'd rush out into the garden and steal her baby again, from right under her nose. But now she smiled quite kindly, in a rather strained way, and waved her arm.

'Sit down,' she said. 'Here, in this chair, by the fire. Doctor Lennard rang and told me you wanted to see me. I didn't want to see you at first, but he persuaded me.'

We both sat down, I with my back to the window. I looked across at her, a plump, homely person, about twenty-five or twenty-six, her fair hair carefully in place, her clothing ordinary. I looked round the room, an ordinary room, with things lying about in it, a pipe, newspapers, some toys.

'Have you other children?' I said, looking at the toys.

'Yes,' she said. 'We've another boy. He's three. My mother took him out for the afternoon.'

'Is the baby all right?' I asked.

'Yes, he's perfectly all right. You looked after him well. I could see that. It was me who wasn't all right.'

A bleak expression came into her face and I thought of what it must have been like for her to come out of that shop and find her child gone.

'It seems silly just to say I'm sorry,' I said, 'because I know it's not enough. I know what an awful thing I did. All I can say is that I must have been a little mad at the time. But I promise you I never harmed a hair of his head.'

'No, I know you didn't,' she said. 'Now. But at the time, I thought I'd never forgive you. And when I heard you wanted to come and see me, I said no. I said I never wanted to meet such a crazy woman who could do such a thing. Ever. I said some horrible things, but now you're here, it's not quite the same. You seem just like anyone else. And I thought you'd be some kind of maniac with staring eyes, or something. I suppose I've not been quite right in the head lately either.'

She laughed then. A happy laugh which showed what she was usually like. I laughed too, a laugh of relief really. Here we were, the two of us, not very different, except she had two children and I had none.

She got up and went to make some tea. I followed her into the kitchen and soon we were talking as if we'd been friends for quite a time. She told me about her other little boy and what hard work it was with two, and how her husband worked a long way away and was often late back.

'But it's not too bad,' she said. 'My mother helps a bit and gives me a bit of time off. And she takes Dennis off for walks like this sometimes.'

'Didn't you want him to see me?' I said.

She looked at me quickly and then smiled.

'No, not really. But then I didn't know what you were like, did I? Do you want to see the baby?'

I shook my head, and she looked surprised. She did not really understand either. It was not her beautiful baby that I wanted. At the time, *any* baby would have been the same to me. And now I was almost a different person. I stayed a little longer and then I said goodbye. I thanked her for being so kind.

'I wasn't kind really,' she said honestly. 'I hated you at first. Hated you. But not now. I've got over that. And you can't go on hating a person you don't even know, can you?'

I took the bus home. Sam had gone back to work and he would be in soon. The days dragged on and we still did not know if a charge were being brought against me. Although we were anxious, somehow I felt much better. As if the air had cleared. I had decided to get a job, if I could. If I were allowed to. I would have to look hard at myself and if I were to change, then the only person who could do the changing was me, myself. Not anyone else.

It was difficult, and I worried quite a lot. I always thought you could not change people. But that was other people. If I wanted to change myself, then I was the only person who could do it. Sam would help, of course. Of course.

Sam came back at the usual time. I opened the door as usual, he kissed me and hung up his coat. Then he went to wash. When he came back, we sat down for our meal.

'Hullo, Jo Bent,' he said. 'How's things?'

'Sticky,' I said. 'But better.'

'Well, what's for tea?' he went on. 'I'm hungry.'

'Fish,' I said. 'It was quick to do. I've been out.'

Sam wrinkled up his nose. He was not very fond of fish.

'Oh well,' he said. 'Better than nothing. I'll survive.'

When we were washing up, Sam dropped another dish. The crash startled me. I turned round to find him standing there, grinning at me.

I looked up at him, and then at the broken bits of dish on the floor.

'Go on,' I said. 'Pick them up yourself, you clumsy brute.'

His eyebrows shot up and he smiled.

'Well, that's a start,' he said gently. 'It's not going to be easy, you know, Jo. Picking up the bits. But as long as we're both heading in the same direction, perhaps we'll get there in the end.'

Tears are strange things. The last time I could remember crying was in the car, when I was being taken to Sam's house in Manchester. When I was ten. Perhaps it was a good sign, because that had turned out well for me. Perhaps this would too.

more TOPLINERS for your enjoyment

by E. W. HILDICK
Birdy Jones
Meet Birdy Jones, the one and only Pop Whistler in the business.

Birdy and the Group
Birdy and the Breakers enter the Battle of the Groups — this one blows the Pop world wide open!

Louie's Lot
Will Tim make Louie's Lot? A savage dog and a masked raider are only two of his tests.

'Louies S.O.S.
The case of the Dirty Milk Bottles and how Louie's Lot rallied round.

by IRMA CHILTON
String of Time
Gill's motor-bike crash lands her in a terrifying nightmare world . . .

by REGINALD MADDOCK
The Dragon in the Garden
The explosive story of Jimmy, who even learns judo to fend off Fagso Brown.

by RAY POPE
The Drum
England invaded . . . Four boys and a girl struggle for survival.

TOPLINERS published by Pan/Macmillan

a Ross.

Sam and Me

The story opens with Jo alone with a baby in an ugly furnished room. In the room, she vividly relives the events which have brought her there. She remembers her childhood in children's 'homes' — and how happy she was when at last she found a real family. She remembers how she got to know Sam . . . Why are she and Sam separated now? As this moving and unusual story develops, both Jo and the reader discover the answer to this important question.

To Dumper